Your Point Is?

JIM DAVIS

ЯR
RAVETTE PUBLISHING

First published by Ravette Publishing 2013.

Printed in the UK by CPI Group (UK) Ltd, Croydon, CR0 4YY
for Ravette Publishing Limited,
PO Box 876
Horsham
West Sussex RH12 9GH

ISBN: 978-1-84161-370-3

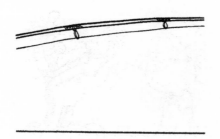

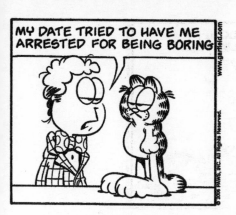

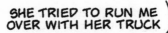

BETTER WISH
FOR MORE
SAND THIS
YEAR

HEE
HEE
HEE

I HATE
BIRTHDAY
NIGHTMARES

OTHER GARFIELD BOOKS AVAILABLE

Pocket Books		Price	ISBN
Am I Bothered?		£3.99	978-1-84161-286-7
Don't Ask!		£3.99	978-1-84161-247-8
Feed Me!		£3.99	978-1-84161-242-3
Going for Gold	(new)	£3.99	978-1-84161-364-2
Gooooal!		£3.99	978-1-84161-329-1
Gotcha!		£3.50	978-1-84161-226-3
I Am What I Am!		£3.99	978-1-84161-243-0
Kowabunga		£3.99	978-1-84161-246-1
Numero Uno		£3.99	978-1-84161-297-3
S.W.A.L.K.		£3.50	978-1-84161-225-6
Talk to the Paw		£3.99	978-1-84161-317-8
Time to Delegate		£3.99	978-1-84161-296-6
Wan2tlk?		£3.99	978-1-84161-264-5
Wassup?		£3.99	978-1-84161-355-0
Whatever!		£3.99	978-1-84161-330-7

Classics	Price	ISBN
Volume One	£7.99	978-1-85304-970-5
Volume Two	£7.99	978-1-85304-971-2
Volume Three	£7.99	978-1-85304-996-5
Volume Four	£7.99	978-1-85304-997-2
Volume Five	£7.99	978-1-84161-022-1
Volume Six	£7.99	978-1-84161-023-8
Volume Seven	£7.99	978-1-84161-088-7
Volume Eight	£7.99	978-1-84161-089-4
Volume Nine	£7.99	978-1-84161-149-5
Volume Ten	£7.99	978-1-84161-150-1
Volume Eleven	£7.99	978-1-84161-175-4
Volume Twelve	£7.99	978-1-84161-176-1
Volume Thirteen	£7.99	978-1-84161-206-5
Volume Fourteen	£7.99	978-1-84161-207-2
Volume Fifteen	£5.99	978-1-84161-232-4
Volume Sixteen	£5.99	978-1-84161-233-1
Volume Seventeen	£7.99	978-1-84161-250-8
Volume Eighteen	£7.99	978-1-84161 251-5
Volume Nineteen	£7.99	978-1-84161-303-1
Volume Twenty	£6.99	978-1-84161 304-8
Volume Twenty One	£7.99	978-1-84161-359-8

Miscellaneous	Price	ISBN
Colour Collection Book 3	£11.99	978-1-84161-320-8
Colour Collection Book 2	£10.99	978-1-84161-306-2
Colour Collection Book 1	£10.99	978-1-84161-293-5
Garfield & Co (Graphic Novel)	£6.99	978-1-84161-349-9